How to Give the Perfect Foot Massage

A GIFT OF LOVE

By Stacey Saleff

Illustrations by Liz Grace

Lawrence Teacher Books
=== Philadelphia ===

Mechanicals produced by book soup publishing, inc.

Cover and interior design by Nancy Loggins Gonzalez
Illustrations © 2001 by Liz Grace

Edited by Erin Slonaker

ISBN 1-930408-26-9

10 9 8 7 6 5 4 3 2 1

Contents

How to Give the Perfect Foot Massage

Contents

Introduction

"Have a heart that never hardens, a temper that never tires, a touch that never hurts."

—Charles Dickens
British writer (1812-1870)

We all know how important touch is to our daily well-being. It can be therapeutic, comforting, and can help us

9

feel a little closer to our loved ones.

A foot massage—the perfect gift of love—is one of the best and most time-honored methods we have to introduce touch and comfort into our most important relationships. Whether you use it as a morning energizer, an afternoon refresher, or a late evening relaxer, a great foot massage is always a welcome treat.

Massaging the feet of a partner or close friend is almost better than an

outright declaration of love. When you give someone a foot massage, your entire focus is on them—and in the process, the connection between you grows even stronger. Without saying a word, you've shown the extent of your caring.

Use this tiny tome as a starting point for more foot massages. Within these pages you'll learn some basic techniques that anyone can master. You'll also find

out about the many added aspects of a massage experience that you can choose to use, including aromatherapy, reflexology, and creating a relaxing atmosphere. The rest is up to you.

Take the time to connect with your loved one through the feet—make the exchange of foot massages a sacred ritual, shared only between the two of you. Perform the ritual regularly—set aside time especially for it.

Make up new techniques on your own, find the scent that inspires just the right mood, even learn which music will augment the experience, and most of all, enjoy it.

Exchange this gift of love today, tomorrow, and for your lifetime together.

Some Facts of Massage

Touch is a vital part of life. From birth, in fact, touch is crucial to our development. Massage—the art used to relax the body or promote circulation—is the ultimate form of touch.

Studies have shown that premature babies grow 47 percent faster when massaged regularly, and massage can have beneficial effects for those with depression, difficulty sleeping, or high

levels of stress. A massage increases the production of the chemical serotonin, which strengthens the immune system. After massage, people often notice an improvement in mood and enjoy a relaxing attitude adjustment.

Many ancient cultures used massage as a healing practice—often administered with herbs and oils by the tribal healer. (No doubt the first massage was undocumented, and occurred when

a cavewoman patted a toe she stubbed while rearranging boulders in her bedroom.) Literature from Egypt, India, China, and Persia documents the ancient use of massage. Julius Caesar wasn't missing out either, receiving daily massage for his epilepsy and neuralgia. Massage was passed on to all of western culture by the Greek physician Hippocrates, the father of modern medicine, who recommended

its use by every physician.

Egyptian hieroglyphics have been found which appear to depict foot massage as a treatment for shoulder pain. Massage was so important to the ancient Jews that the root word for rubbing with oils and for the Messiah are the same. The Christians also used massage, calling it the "laying on of hands."

Modern massage can be traced to the

Frenchman Ambroise Paré, one of the founders of modern surgery. In the late eighteenth century, Per Henrik Ling of Sweden founded a school which incorporates the use of movement and massage for healing. Ling didn't actually invent massage, but he gathered various techniques and helped achieve recognition for massage throughout the world.

The Why, When, and Where of Foot Massage

Why the Feet?

Supporting the full weight of our bodies every step we take, our feet deserve a hand. Feet are quite small compared to the bodies they support; Leonardo da Vinci felt that the foot was a work of art, a masterpiece of engineering. And yet the feet continue to be overworked and neglected. We subject them to the demands of fashion,

squeezing and cramming them into shoes where they just don't belong. It's fitting that a person's one weakness is called the "Achilles Heel," as many of us become miserable when our feet hurt.

The effect our feet have on our whole bodies is understandable, considering that most of the body's nerves—about 72,000 of them—have endings in the feet. A foot massage helps ease the tension out of not only the feet, but the whole body as well.

Foot massage is an excellent way for everyone to incorporate touch into their lives. It's easy to learn and can be safely practiced by the non-professional. Nothing impresses your loved ones more than offering to pamper them with a much-needed foot massage!

Foot massage is a safe way for two people to connect (or reconnect, as the case may be), and it can also promote general health for the whole body.

One system of foot massage, known as reflexology, suggests that working out a sore spot on your foot could correspond to the healing of a troublesome joint, organ, or muscle elsewhere in the body. The simple foot, then, has a greater role in well-being than one would think.

When—Perfect Timing

The timing of when to give a foot massage depends on many things—the time of day, your alertness, even how long you've known your partner. An early morning foot massage may be the perfect thing to prepare you for the day. Refreshed after a night's sleep, the feet can benefit from some added love and care, and whoever

Cuddle Chemical—We are actually chemically induced to give and receive touch by oxytocin, the hormone that helps to inseparably bond mothers and their nursing babies. Oxytocin is also an important bonding agent in romantic love, compelling people to couple. Massage is an excellent way to satisfy this need.

receives the massage can spend the day feeling light as a feather. After work or before bed, the foot massage can ease out the built-up tension of the day and rest the mind and body for a good night's rest.

Depending on the particular techniques you employ, you can make your foot massage either invigorating or relaxing—it's all up to you. Pick a time when you can work uninterrupted, be

it for a half hour or longer. Even fifteen minutes is enough time for a worthwhile foot massage, and you'll appreciate whatever time you devote to it in the long run.

More endorphins, please—Also associated with touch, these morphine-like opiates of the mind calm and reassure.

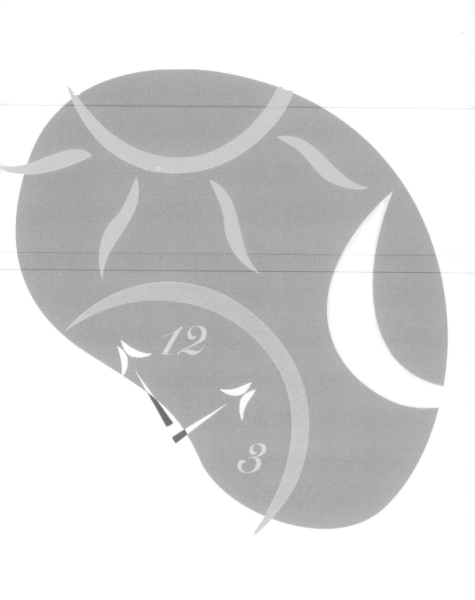

It's also helpful to look at the progress of your relationship with your partner to determine the timing of a foot massage. Massaging increases trust and relaxation, and it is a pleasant way to spend some casual time together.

Massage is also a good prelude to conversations that may involve important topics. A potentially stressful situation can be buffered by first exchanging a foot massage; it leaves one more relaxed,

likely to listen better, even agreeable!

There are many times in an already established relationship that are perfect for sharing a massage. If you've just moved in together, you may be grappling with the shift in responsibility and personal space. A way to counteract those new feelings is to actually come together to create a shared ritual of foot massage. It provides a personal moment of relaxation, and at the same

time enables you to better interact, cooperate, and compromise.

Later in the relationship—even many years later—old patterns can give way to soothing touch. A foot massage can bypass normal daily interactions and convey "I love you" without the words. No matter what your mood, a loving message is sent, and it is almost certain to be returned in kind. In fact, the physical touch of massage can

bring you out of the foulest of moods, whether you're receiving or giving.

At any time, couples can use massage as a tool to work through rocky stages, from demanding career schedules to empty nest syndrome, from exhausting baby sleep- and non-sleep-patterns to mid-life crises, and from menopause to the golden years. Every stage of life presents a situation where a little extra tender loving care is welcome.

Where to Massage

Anywhere you find yourself with your partner is a fine place to enjoy a foot massage. In the park, on a plane, or even in a restaurant, a foot massage is rarely refused. If you are in a public establishment such as a café or restaurant, a tablecloth might just allow you the privacy to secretly reach your partner's toes. You can, of course, simply

exchange massages while watching tele-
vision on your favorite cozy couch or
on the floor in front of a crackling fire.

    While traveling, it's particularly
delightful to take a breather from sight-
seeing to have your feet rejuvenated,
and nothing feels better on a plane ride
than sliding your legs over an empty
chair between you and your partner
and getting the ache rubbed out of
your tired toes. There are strokes that

can actually reduce the tenderness and swelling caused by the pressurized cabin. Long car trips are an excellent time to practice massage, as long as neither of you is driving!

Spontaneous foot rubs are always fun. Surprise visits from friends—who are interested in rubbing your feet—are always welcome. A friend who will rub your feet if they gravitate into his or her vicinity is a cherished friend indeed.

Create a Sacred Space

It is possible to take massage to another level, and create a ritual at home. Set time aside to create a complete experience, and this can become more than a foot rub. Choose a room you are comfortable in and set up a special environment.

Disconnect

Turn off the ringer on the phone, put the pager on mute, and let the doorbell

go unanswered. Be sure to arrange
your responsibilities so that you will
not be missed for an hour. The idea is
a session of complete peace, to be vio-
lated under no ordinary circumstances.

Lighting

You and your partner need to relax in a
space that's bathed in warm, soft lighting. If you have no dimmer switch or
soft light bulbs, play with the lighting

possibilities. Place a non-halogen lamp behind the curtains if you can (don't let the curtains touch the bulb), or even plug in a string of white or gold holiday lights to be draped temporarily around the room. Candles also provide perfect lighting. You might use several to properly illuminate the room. Creative lighting sets the tone, creating a feeling of safety and warmth.

Good Scents

Aromatherapy is the therapeutic use of pure essential oils, which are the distilled essences of herbs. Products are available at many stores and web-sites that sell candles, soaps, and bath products. To make the most of your aromatic experience, make sure your purchases contain essential oils. Beware of chemical imitations that do not give

the benefits of herbal aromatherapy; they can be neurotoxic.

The smell of roses is said to be good for many things, including depression, headache, constipation, frigidity, impotence, and even skincare—it's no surprise men have been giving women roses for thousands of years!

If you decide to experiment and mix oils yourself, you are in for an adventure. Essential oil is not cheap, but the combinations and variations are endless. Essential oils are so strong, one need only use a few drops at a time, so one small vial will last a very long time. Use a small glass or ceramic bowl to combine a few drops of essential oil with a couple tablespoons of your favorite unscented lotion or oil.

Lotion may be best for the feet because it's less slippery. If you do decide to use oil, a good rule of thumb is to use one that's edible, since it can penetrate into your bloodstream through the skin. Sesame, sweet almond, and grapeseed oils are the favorites of massage professionals.

If you choose the premixed route, there are many nice lotions available specifically for the feet that you can

buy at specialty beauty stores, drug-stores, or on the web.

Essential oils have been used since ancient times; they are a good way to apply herbs for medicinal or relaxation purposes. Of the many scents available, here are a few which you might like to try. The scents of rose, yang-ylang, jasmine, and sandalwood are aphrodisi-acs. Geranium is relaxing and refreshing. Lavender is good for physical and

nervous fatigue. Peppermint is cooling and refreshing, and is so perfect for tired, overheated feet that many foot lotions contain it. Tea tree oil deodorizes and can work against fungus.

Incense is another way to add a pleasant aroma to the atmosphere. Nag-Champa is understandably a popular incense, as it is said to produce happiness. (Burn it for only a few minutes, instead of letting it burn itself out—after a few

minutes the smell can be too strong, and the incense can smoke up the room.)

Mentha-lated romance—Greek mythology romantically describes peppermint as originating from the nymph Mentha, with whom Hades was enamored. His jealous wife, Persephone, tread on Mentha, so Hades turned her into the flavorful foliage.

In Tune

In creating a complete sensory experience, the element of sound is as important as the lighting. Playing any music that you both enjoy is suitable. Choose something soft and low-key if you want background music to augment the experience, not overpower it. Select something a bit more symphonic or dynamic if you want to use the music for inspiration.

Remember that different musical instruments tend to affect different parts of the body. Drums simulate the beat of the heart and can speed, impassion, or sedate it. The bass seems to speak directly to the pelvis; sultry music with lots of slow, heavy bass tones may be conducive to a passionate evening. While some find violins romantic, others find them ear-piercing.

Play music that's appropriate for

the level of your courtship. If it's a new
relationship, not passionately intimate,
you may select more melodic or lighthearted music. Nature sounds, classical,
or New Age music are popular for
massage and are available in most music
stores. Soft ocean wave recordings can
be almost hypnotic. Classical music has
a tremendous ability to evoke strong
emotions, so choose carefully. Debussy,
Brahms, Pachelbel, or Chopin, who

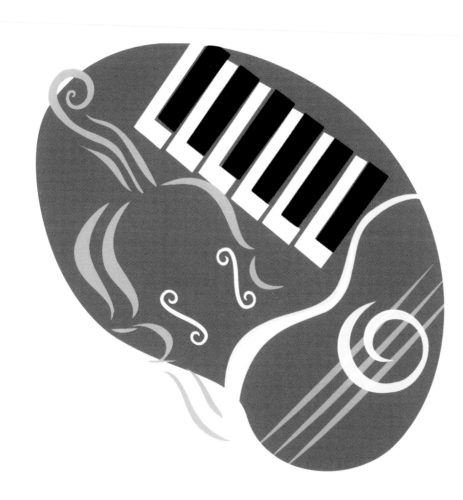

have all composed more lighthearted piano pieces, would all be good choices. Tibetan bells set a meditative tone, as do Native American or Asian flutes.

The thing to remember is to play the music that pleases you both, be it drum and bass, hip-hop, or Connie Francis.

Enjoy the Work!

Once the atmosphere is established, the work is done. Even for the massager, the rest is play. Just as a gardener provides proper light, rich soil, appropriate climate, and compassionate tending, you have set the stage for the flow of natural life energy. Just as the gardener's seeds know how to grow, your heart's energy knows just how to

flow to your partner through your hands.

While massaging, imagine the loving energy of the heart flowing freely through the hands. In this context, it's easy to understand the significance of the European tradition of giving one's hand in marriage.

Basic Foot Massage

What You Need

Ready Hands and Feet

Willing hands and feet are all you need to provide a foot massage that will not be forgotten. Before applying lotion, be sure to wash your hands with soap and warm water. Even if you feel that your hands are clean, it's good to wash away germs.

The massagee's feet may need washing with a warm cloth after wear-

ing shoes all day. For the spa-minded massager, wrap the feet in hot towels or give a foot-bath scented with soothing oils. If using lotion or oil, it's a good idea to place a small towel under the feet, so as not to get oil or lotion on the pillow, hassock, or lap on which they are resting.

Make sure all nails are filed smooth and preferably short. Long fingernails can be kept, but you won't be able to

give additional pressure in certain strokes, such as thumb circles. With long fingernails, you must make sure to focus on using the pad of the fingers, and quite carefully!

The massagee always needs smooth toenails as well, so as not to scratch the massager's hardworking hands. Avoid working on any injuries on the feet which massage won't help, such as cuts or blisters.

Lotion

Any body lotion can be used, although (as mentioned earlier) you can experiment with ones designed specifically for the feet. First rub hands together to warm them, then smooth the lotion over the surface of your hands; use a small

amount, just enough to allow a smooth, gliding stroke. Apply more lotion as needed, always maintaining reassuring contact with the foot. (Gently rest the back of the hand on the top of the foot as you apply lotion to your palm.)

Proper Positioning

One of the secrets to a great massage is proper body positioning. Sitting straight

in a firm chair or couch, the massager can remain alert and focused without tiring quickly. The massagee should sit or, preferably, recline with feet elevated. The feet need to be easy for the massager to reach naturally, and should lie somewhere between the massager's lap and chest.

The techniques described in this book will assume you are facing each other in a straight line. You may need to

modify the techniques if you are not sitting face to face. It's equally important for both partners to be comfortable, so play with positioning until you get it right. Having the massager sit on a foot stool or hassock, with the massagee resting in a recliner, is perfect. If you don't have a reclining chair, try having the massager sit on the floor, with his or her back against a couch or wall, with the massagee lying on the floor, knees

resting on several soft pillows. Whatever your favorite configuration, it's a good idea to have your knees supported when receiving.

Attentive Ears, Fingers, and More

When giving a massage, let your emotions pour out of your hands. Use gentle, firm pressure as you explore each foot. As the fingertips develop

sympathy for the feet, you will instinctively gravitate to areas in need of attention. If your hands are listening, you can be confident that you will give the perfect foot massage.

For an even greater connection, match your breathing to your partner's. A few deep, relaxing belly breaths (see page 74), while gazing lovingly into your partner's eyes, nourish the soul.

While massaging, it's fine to inquire

about your partner's sensitivity to pressure. Some people prefer feather-like pressure. Others would rather you pushed far deeper than would seem comfortable. Remember, nothing you do should hurt. Even if the massagee says "deeper," watch for signals in the body that the pressure is too much.

Such signals include curling toes, holding the breath, and grimacing. It is common for most of us not to know

Belly Breathing

This type of breathing is deeply relaxing. Not only does it bring more fresh oxygen to each cell and relax your abdominal organs, it's also fun. (You get to stick your belly out like you did when you were five, having a contest with your best friend to see whose was bigger.) Take a breath deep into your belly, pushing out the abdomen, ribs, and then chest. Then exhale naturally, slowly, completely relaxing the torso. Let the chest fall, fall, fall, and eventually, by

squeezing in the abdomen tightly, push all the air out of the lungs. Without pausing, roll the breath into an inhale, and repeat the cycle a few times. This type of breathing is a great way to fully oxygenate the lungs, removing the stale air that can remain when breathing is shallow.

This breathing might seem awkward at first, but practice makes it easier. You don't have to sustain this type of breathing throughout the massage. It's merely helpful as a cleansing start to the foot rub.

where our tender spots are until they
are touched.

The face is the

best pain-meter

of all—signs of distress

will show up there first.

While receiving a massage, be sure to encourage your partner with sounds. Words can be distracting—the appropriate sound is all you need to tell the massager to lighten up or not change a stroke. It's okay to say "umm," "ow!" or "ahhh." A little encouragement is the best way to lengthen the time your partner is willing to work on your feet. (It also helps if your partner knows you'll soon be returning the favor in kind.)

Feel The Energy

nergy is a concept that eludes many people, but in reality it's not so mysterious. We feel energy every day of our lives. In our bodies, energy is experienced as warmth, tingling, or an electrical surge. Our body's senses receive information in the form of energy, be it the passage of light rays through the optical nerve or the detec-

tion of a soft breeze by the delicate nerve receptors on one's arm.

In traditional Chinese medicine, this energy, or life force, is called *chi* (pronounced "chee"), and the quality of one's health is determined by the ability of this energy to flow unobstructedly. Whether we know it or not, we all have energy pulsing through us all the time. In fact, any scientist will tell you that the solid mass we perceive as our

bodies is not solid at all, but a whirling configuration of speeding electrons, electrically charged particles in constant motion.

Tight spots in the body are places where the energy has become stuck. Stuck energy may be experienced as stiffness or it may be painful to the touch. Such areas could use a little massage. Explore the spot tenderly and firmly, careful not to hurt your partner.

Sometimes a lighter touch is even more effective than a deep stroke in these areas, the light touch sensation overriding the painful one. Working on a tight area will help to increase the flow of energy within the body.

As a massagee, you can even transfer some of your own energy into the feet and body of the massagee, and this will only serve to maximize the energy flow in and around you both. Before

beginning the massage, it is a good idea to sit quietly for a moment. Calm your mind and notice your breathing. Allow any tension to flow out with the breath. Try to imagine the oxygen flow from the lungs through the whole body. This will promote relaxation and an even flow of energy.

Remember that couple's massage has no formal rules—one has only to allow and enjoy the natural flow of life energy

and become connected to each other in a new way.

Reflexology—An Advanced Basic of Foot Massage

Reflexology is based on the idea that feet are miniature representations of the entire body—so caring for your partner's feet is an indirect way

to gently caress the whole body. It's a more technical approach to foot massage, and could be incorporated into your routine as you become more adept.

In reflexology, the big toes represent the head and neck, and the organs are placed proportionately to their location on the body. For example, the liver is on the right foot and the heart on the left.

The reflexologist inches the side of the thumb over the foot, exploring it

for trouble spots. Tenderness indicates a deposit of waste materials that have crystallized, like snowflakes.

Massaging these crystals breaks them up and restores a positive and free energy flow through the foot and the corresponding organ or body part.

You should never replace proper medical care with reflexology, and particularly painful symptoms in your body should be addressed by a doctor.

But it's fun to see if your sore back can be alleviated with some special attention to your arches, and to find out if your headache goes away after some focus on your big toes. Alternatively, you can learn more about your body by studying any sore spots on your foot by studying a foot map.

Use reflexology as a supplement if you want to, but don't try to cure all that ails your partner with it!

A word of caution to anyone whose is,

or whose partner may be pregnant:

Working reflexology on the reproductive

organ reflexes in the ankle can bring

on menstruation, a possibly dangerous

effect if she is carrying a child. It's best

to not use deep pressure anywhere on the

foot of a pregnant woman, and only

very light touches on the ankle.

The Massage

nce the massage has begun, always maintain contact, even if it's just with one hand. This touch is reassuring, and it lets your partner know you're still connected even when you briefly stop massaging.

The sequence of strokes described here is designed to begin by warming the feet, then stretching them. It feels great to have the foot treated as a whole before getting to specific or

individual parts. With more and more practice of the techniques, your skills will continue to evolve, which is rewarding for you and a joy for your partner.

Keep in mind that, depending on the massage, the results can be either invigorating or relaxing. Fast strokes with deep pressure will tend to wake your partner up by stimulating the nervous system. This is a great way to

start the day, or have a late afternoon refresher. By nightfall, use a less rigorous pressure and calming pace to help your partner relax. Massaging the feet of a person who is very tired could put him or her right to sleep; quite often foot massage is faster acting than melatonin.

In couple's massage you know you're on the right track when there's a smile on your partner's face. Remember,

there is no such thing as a single "proper technique." Here are the moves you may use to comprise your perfect foot massage.

Symmetry

The techniques should be performed on each foot in turn, so that each foot receives the same attention and balance is maintained.

The Techniques

All Hands on Feet

The first touch sets the tone for the entire session, so the massager's hands should be warm, dry, and supple. This sends a message to the autonomic nervous system that a warm, loving friend is offering comfort, and that it's okay to relax. Let the first contact simply be to rest your hands on your part-

ner's feet. Take a breath and focus for a moment in silence, allowing your body to relax and your mind to become still.

To begin, place your hands on the top of each foot, and use long, gentle strokes up to the ankle and calf, alternating left and right, with or without lotion. This gently prepares the feet for the delight they are about to receive.

This is also an excellent stroke to use on a plane or after a day of walking;

repeated motion up the leg encourages extra fluid to leave the foot and may reduce tenderness.

Fire Starter

Rub your hands together to warm them up. If your partner's feet need warming, and usually they will, rub vigorously with your palms in quick back and forth motions all over each side of the feet.

Warming the feet makes the muscles more relaxed and ready to be massaged.

On Point

While steadying the foot by holding the heel, flex the foot by pointing the toes toward the massagee's nose (A).

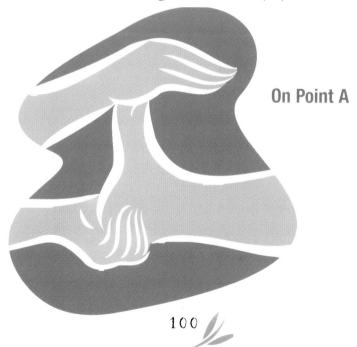

On Point A

100

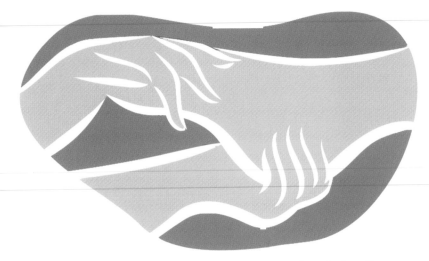

On Point B

Next, stretch the whole foot by pointing the toes away from the massagee's body (B).

Prayer Position

Begin by spreading lotion on your hands in a prayer position. Initiate contact with the fingertips first, gliding the foot between the hands. Pretend your hands are magnets squeezing the foot together from top and bottom. This is a connecting touch that is useful at the beginning of the session—it allows you to loosen up the foot and reduce over-

sensitivity in ticklish people by getting "underneath the tickle."

Twist the Night Away

While in the Prayer Position, interlace fingers and cup the big toe and the ball of the foot so that they are nestled close to the joined fingers. Maintaining a broad palm contact, twist the entire foot outward until your partner feels a relaxing stretch.

Peeling a Grapefruit

With thumbs together

in the middle

of the foot,

press into

the sole

while

pulling

apart, as if

peeling fruit.

The Wave

Gently grasp the foot, with fingers on top and thumb below, slowly pulling your hands toward you. Alternate hands to give a wave-like sensation.

Rhythmic Transitioning

Use The Wave often, especially between other strokes. This technique feels great, adds continuity between strokes, and can relax the entire nervous system.

Perfect Pull

Alternately pull thumbs across the bottom of the foot, moving the right hand from left to right, and the left hand

from right to left—first softly, then more firmly, to more of a pressure sensation. Be sure to cover the entire sole of the foot.

Spiral Style

"Draw" circles on the bottom of the foot with the thumb, starting small and spiraling out to the edges of the foot. Your partner may prefer a firm touch for this stroke.

March Down the Arch

Using your thumb, firmly glide down the arch from the ball of the foot to the inner heel.

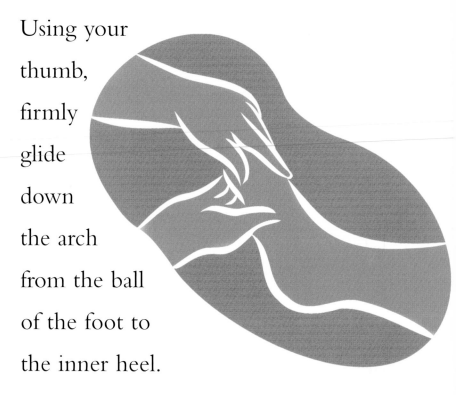

Please Squeeze

Starting with the big toe,

squeeze the top

of the toe

with a

circular

motion.

Be sure

to cover

the

entire

surface of the tip of the toe. Then, squeezing the toe, pull from the base to the tip. Repeat this stroke on the other four toes.

Tug of War

For a more advanced step, try combining the toe squeeze with an arch glide: Both thumbs start at base of the big toe and pull in opposite directions.

Tiny Circles

With your hand gently pressing on the top of the foot, "draw" circles with all of your fingers at once. Imagine tiny spirals drawn from the fingertips. Go from the top of the toes up to the ankle, around the top of the ankle, under to the Achilles tendon,

and back up to the front again.

Shake, Shake, Shake

Brace the heels of your hands just below the ankle bones and alternately move your hands up and down about an inch, in short, quick movements. This technique is not easy at first, but you'll know you've got it when the foot shakes back and forth and you're moving your hands as fast as you can.

Percussion

Gently tap the bottoms of the feet with your knuckles, letting your hand go limp and flicking your wrist so that the weight of the knuckles falls on the foot.

Waterfall

With long, light strokes, simulate the feeling of a cool waterfall along the top side of each foot, using feather-weight strokes with the fingertips from

the mid-calf to the toes. Waterfall each foot singly and then both simultaneously, with the pressure gradually growing lighter.

Over So Soon?

No time passes as quickly as the time spent receiving a massage. Be kind to your partner and linger over the final moments.

The Final Touch!

A delightful last touch involves simply resting your hands comfortably on the feet. Take a breath and relax away any tension in your body. Focus on sensing the energy exchange between your partner's feet and your hands. You may feel warmth or even heat. That's good: It's your body's energy building. Rest your hands there as long as you like.

To remove them, lift the hands as slowly and imperceptibly as you can. With practice, your hands will feel as if they are floating up of their own accord, and your partner won't know you have lifted your hands away!

Conclusion

Now that you've learned some of the secrets of a fabulous massage, make sure to practice. The minutes, hours, and even years will be more rewarding than you can imagine! Don't forget to experiment: try out new moves that you make up yourself, explore painful

spots as they occur, and customize the foot massage until it's just right. Remember that, as in any relationship, there is room for growth and change. Sometimes those changes make the experience even better.

Foot massage is a fun and meaningful way to connect at any stage of courtship. In an age requiring new standards for dating rituals, foot massage is a safe and enjoyable pastime and an

expression of love.

Foot massage is all about connecting with another person; it's about feeling what they feel, giving some of yourself to another—it's simply a gift of love.

How To Give the Perfect Foot Massage